Smelly Spelling
Louis Fidge

In a hidden cave, far away in a magical land, lives a wise wizard, called Whimstaff. Every now and again, he searches for a young apprentice, so he can pass on his magical English powers. And this time, Whimstaff has chosen you!

Whimstaff shares the cave with a goblin and a little red dragon. Pointy, the goblin, is very clever. The dragon, called Miss Snufflebeam, breathes small puffs of fire. She is clumsy and often loses the wizard's magical letters and numbers.

Pointy has two greedy, pet frogs, called Mugly and Bugly, who are very lazy and spend most of their time croaking, eating and sleeping. But every so often, they amaze Pointy by helping with an exercise!

Wizard Whimstaff and his friends are very happy in their cave, solving English problems. Join them on a magical quest to become a fully qualified English wizard!

Contents

Letts

Wiggly Words

Hello, I'm Wizard Whimstaff and
I want to help you with your spelling.
If you look carefully you can
often find small words hiding
inside long words.

Can you find <u>cat</u> and <u>pill</u> in <u>caterpillar</u>?

Task 1 Allakazan! Find and circle the names of these animals hiding in the
words below.

duck

otter

rat

bat

hen

ant

owl

ape

| **a** bowl | **b** spotter | **c** bath | **d** rather |
| **e** when | **f** elephant | **g** ducked | **h** escape |

Task 2 Now try this, my apprentice. Add a letter to each of these words to
make the name of an animal.

a <u>c</u>at   **b** do__   **c** __oat   **d** sea__   **e** came__   **f** badge__

⭐ Task 3 Do the best you can on this task. Find a small word hiding in the name of each vegetable.

a potato   **b** carrot   **c** onion   **d** sprout   **e** turnip   **f** cauliflower

_____   _____   _____   _____   _____   _____

⭐ Task 4 Use your magical powers of observation! Find two small words inside each long word.

long word	small words	
a comfortable	*for*	*able*
b bandage	_____	_____
c stare	_____	_____
d attention	_____	_____
e because	_____	_____
f beaten	_____	_____

Sorcerer's Skill Check

Find and underline the word in each set that contains the small word on the left. Hey presto!

a (all)   read   call   open   jump

b (ink)   teacher   two   goat   pink

c (and)   band   sea   table   door

d (luck)   funny   bang   cluck   bell

Croak! Award yourself a gold star
and stick it on your certificate on page 32.

Fearless Feats

We're Mugly and Bugly and this is a brain cell alert! You need to be careful because sometimes ea can be pronounced differently.

feast — Sometimes ea has a long sound.

bread — Sometimes ea has a short sound.

Task 1 Slurp! Help us find and write the rhyming pairs of words with a **long ea** sound.

heap	feast	**a** _____ _____
weak	leap	**b** _heap_ _leap_
beat	leak	**c** _____ _____
tea	sea	**d** _____ _____
beast	heat	**e** _____ _____

Task 2 Now help us find and write the rhyming pairs of words containing a **short ea** sound. Is it time for a snack yet?

head	weather	**a** _____ _____
death	healthy	**b** _____ _____
ready	breath	**c** _____ _____
feather	instead	**d** _head_ _instead_
wealthy	steady	**e** _____ _____

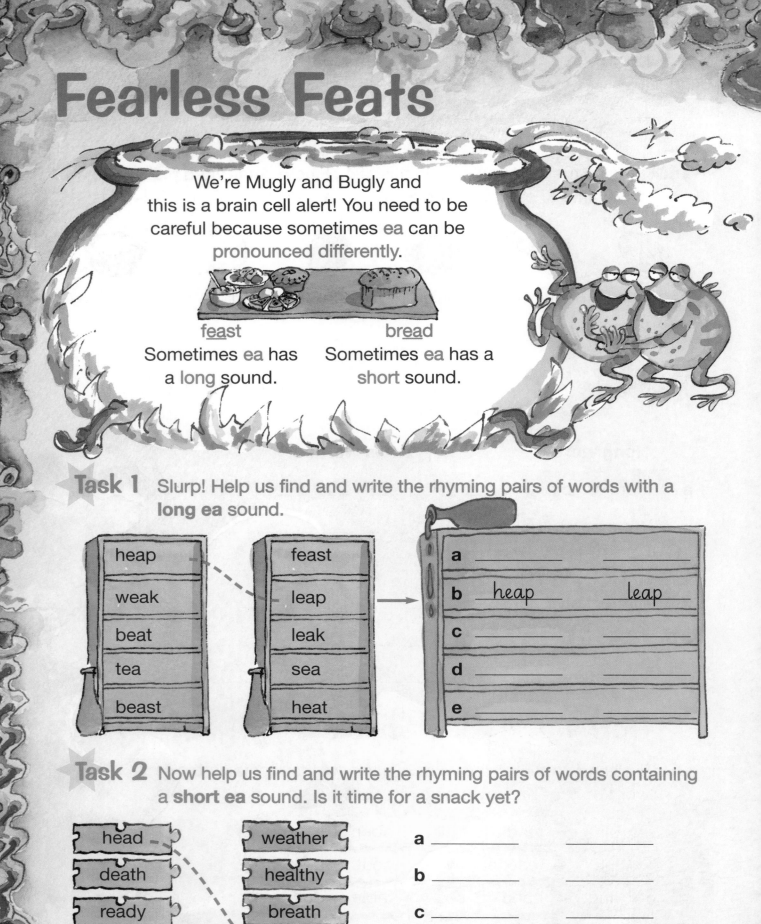

4

Task 3 Make some **ea** words, while we have a bite to eat. Grub's up!

ea

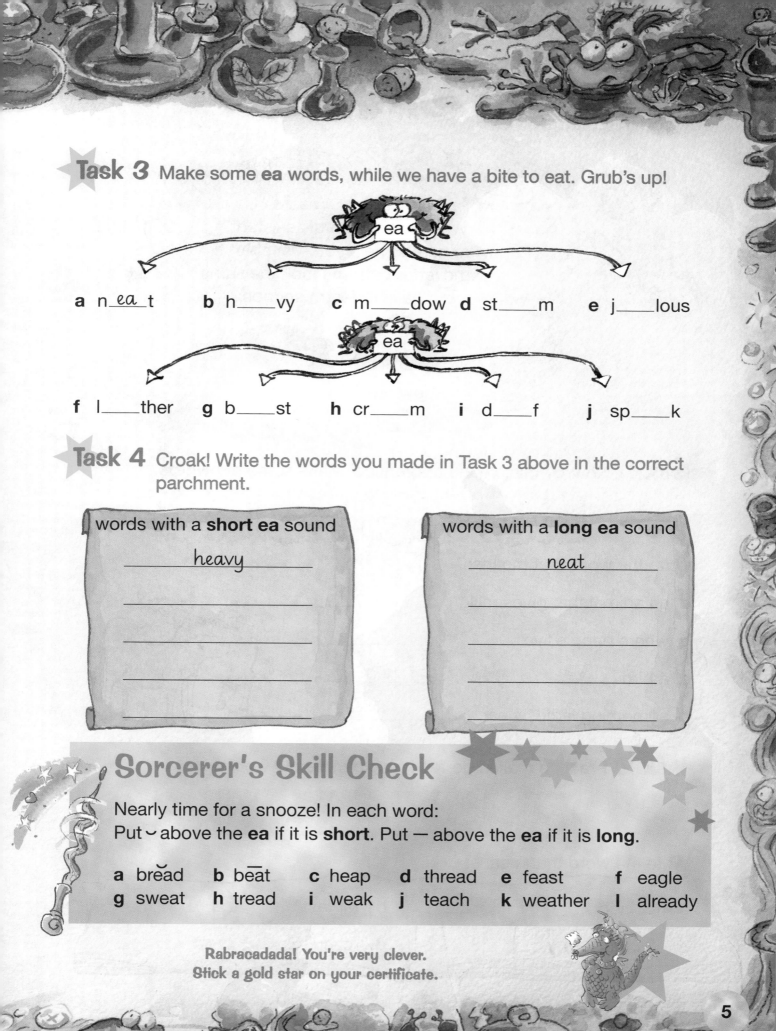

a n_ea_t **b** h____vy **c** m____dow **d** st____m **e** j____lous

ea

f l____ther **g** b____st **h** cr____m **i** d____f **j** sp____k

Task 4 Croak! Write the words you made in Task 3 above in the correct parchment.

words with a **short ea** sound	words with a **long ea** sound
heavy	neat

Sorcerer's Skill Check

Nearly time for a snooze! In each word:
Put ˘ above the **ea** if it is **short**. Put ‾ above the **ea** if it is **long**.

a brĕad **b** bēat **c** heap **d** thread **e** feast **f** eagle
g sweat **h** tread **i** weak **j** teach **k** weather **l** already

Rabracadada! You're very clever.
Stick a gold star on your certificate.

Scowling Shadows

I'm Pointy, Wizard Whimstaff's helpful assistant! I'm here to help you. Watch out! Some letter patterns look the same but have different sounds.

b<u>ow</u> tie   b<u>ow</u>

Task 1 Now try this, young apprentice! Make some **ow** words.

t <u>o</u> <u>w</u> n   g _ _ n   c _ _ _   _ _ l

Write the word that means:

a an animal that gives milk _____

b where people live _____

c a bird _____

d something ladies wear _____

Task 2 Practice makes perfect! Magic more **ow** words.

sl _ _ _   b _ _ l   l _ _   sn _ _

Write the word that means:

a not high _____ **b** not fast _____

c a container _____ **d** frozen rain _____

Task 3 Say each word and listen to the sound the **ow** makes.

low	now	mow	how	brown	snow
slow	shown	cow	growl	crown	blow

Write the **ow** words that sound like the **ow** in **crow** in the blue spell book.

Write the **ow** words that sound like **ow** in **owl** in the red spell book. Super!

Sorcerer's Skill Check

Miss Snufflebeam has mixed up the letters in these words. Can you unscramble the letters and write the words correctly?

a wco   **b** wol   **c** obwl   **d** nswo   **e** erowt   **f** owmre

cow

Slurp! Another gold star! You'll be as brainy as Pointy soon!

Hooks and Books

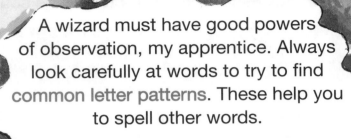

A wizard must have good powers of observation, my apprentice. Always look carefully at words to try to find common letter patterns. These help you to spell other words.

b<u>ook</u>   c<u>ook</u>   h<u>ook</u>

Task 1 Allakazan! Wave your magic wand at these.

Finish the words with **ook**.	Write the words.
a c _ _ _	_____
b b _ _ _	_____
c h _ _ _	_____
d r _ _ _	_____

Finish the words with **ood**.	Write the words.
e h _ _ _	_____
f w _ _ _	_____
g g _ _ _	_____
h st _ _ _	_____

Task 2 Work out which letters are missing from the words below. Do your best magical work!

a a _ _ _ _ _ ery

   b _ _ _

b Red Riding H _ _ _

in the w _ _ _

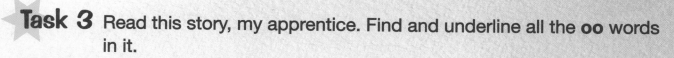

Task 3 Read this story, my apprentice. Find and underline all the **oo** words in it.

One day I took my friend to look for birds in the woods. We wore our coats with hoods. When we stood still we saw many big black rooks near the brook. Suddenly my foot slipped. I fell into the water and shook with cold.

Task 4 Sort the words you found into sets. Hey presto!

a ook words: _____ _____ _____ _____

b ood words: _____ _____ _____

c oot word: _____

Sorcerer's Skill Check

Miss Snufflebeam has got the last letter of each word wrong. Rewrite each word and end it with either **k**, **t** or **d**.

a lood _look_   **e** sood _____   **i** cood _____

b fook _____   **f** blook _____   **j** wook _____

c broot _____   **g** bood _____   **k** croot _____

d gook _____   **h** tood _____   **l** rood _____

Super! You can help yourself to a gold star
for your hard work.

Strange Spaces

I'm Miss Snufflebeam and I'm supposed to tell you what happens to **c** and **g** when they are followed by **e**. I hope I can remember!

Here is my fa<u>ce</u>. Do you know my a<u>ge</u>?

When **c** is followed by **e** it sounds like **s**.
When **g** is followed by **e** it sounds like **j**.

⭐ **Task 1**   Help me make some sets of words. Rabracadada!

a ice words:

n <u>i</u> <u>c</u> <u>e</u>   sl _ _ _   tw _ _ _ _   r _ _ _ _

b ace words:

f _ _ _   pl _ _ _   sp _ _ _   r _ _ _

c age words:

r _ _ _   c _ _ _   p _ _ _   w _ _ _

⭐ **Task 2**   Oh no! Can you help me use some of the words you made in Task 1 above to complete these sentences?

a I like a n ___ ___ ___   sl ___ ___ ___   of cake.

b The parrot was in a c ___ ___ ___ .

c The rocket flew into sp ___ ___ ___ .

d I fell over tw ___ ___ ___   and cut my f ___ ___ ___ .

10

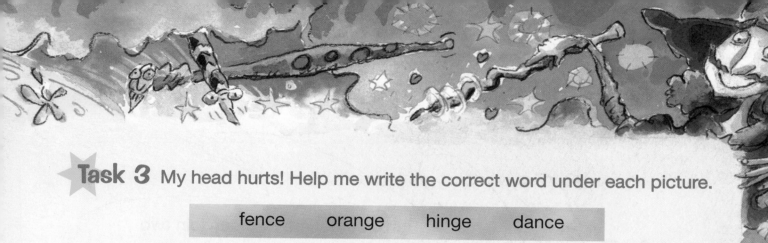

Task 3 My head hurts! Help me write the correct word under each picture.

| fence | orange | hinge | dance |

a 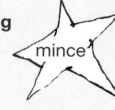 **b** 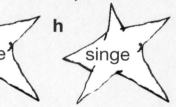 **c**  **d**

_____ _____ _____ _____

Task 4 Dabracababra! Colour the **nce** stars orange and the **nge** stars blue.

a chance   **b** strange   **c** glance   **d** pence   **e** fringe

f plunge   **g** mince   **h** singe   **i** prince   **j** cringe

Sorcerer's Skill Check

Oops! I thought we had finished – but there is just one thing left to do. Complete each word with **ice** or **age**.

a d_____   **e** sl_____   **i** tw_____   **m** pol_____

b m_____   **f** pr_____   **j** off_____   **n** mess_____

c c_____   **g** s_____   **k** st_____   **o** aver_____

d p_____   **h** w_____   **l** cour_____

You are getting on very well, my apprentice.
You deserve a gold star for your efforts!

11

Conjuring Compounds

Burp! Sometimes we can join two small words together to make a longer word. These words are called compound words.

toad + stool = toadstool

Task 1 This must be a job for Pointy! You can try it first – make some compound words.

a snow + man	=	_snowman_	**f** horse + shoe	=	_____
b butter + fly	=	_____	**g** lady + bird	=	_____
c foot + ball	=	_____	**h** key + hole	=	_____
d wind + mill	=	_____	**i** sheep + dog	=	_____
e pan + cake	=	_____	**j** sun + shine	=	_____

Task 2 Slurp! Choose one of the compound words you made in Task 1 above to go under each picture.

a    **b**    **c**    **d**

_____   _____   _____   _____

Task 3 Brain cell alert! Match up the pairs of words to make some compound words.

Write the compound words here.

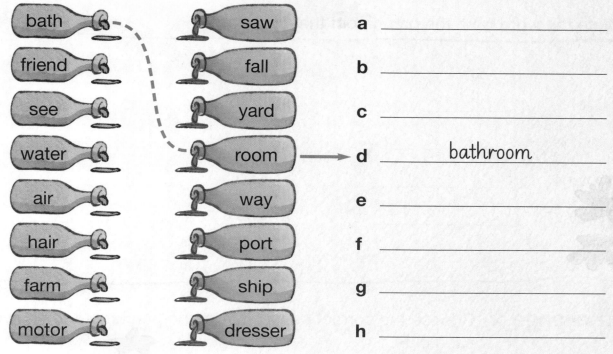

bath	saw
friend	fall
see	yard
water	room
air	way
hair	port
farm	ship
motor	dresser

a _____

b _____

c _____

d _____bathroom_____

e _____

f _____

g _____

h _____

Sorcerer's Skill Check

Write the two small words that make up each compound word.
Is it time for a snooze yet?

a birthday = _____ + _____   f cloakroom = _____ + _____

b farmyard = _____ + _____   g dishcloth = _____ + _____

c wallpaper = _____ + _____   h breakfast = _____ + _____

d buttercup = _____ + _____   i indoors   = _____ + _____

e outside   = _____ + _____   j myself   = _____ + _____

**Your spelling is coming along nicely.
Have a gold star to celebrate! Super!**

Apprentice Wizard Challenge 1

Challenge 1

know	monkey	want	shout	every	friend
father	yellow	many	because	down	suddenly

Write the word from the parchment that contains:

a very _____

b den _____

c ant _____

d own _____

e key _____

f out _____

g fat _____

h now _____

i any _____

j end _____

k use _____

l low _____

Challenge 2 Choose the correct **ea** word from the parchment to answer each clue.

neat	heavy	meadow	peach	speak	cream	leather	deaf

a not light _____

b tidy _____

c a field _____

d animal skin _____

e unable to hear _____

f a fruit _____

g made from milk _____

h to talk _____

Challenge 3 Work out the answers to these sums.

a g + r + ow = _____

b t + ow + n = _____

c c + r + ow + d = _____

d th + r + ow = _____

14

Challenge 4 Change the **l** in look to:

a c _____cook_____

b t _____

c h _____

d r _____

e b _____

f n _____

g sh _____

h cr _____

i br _____

Challenge 5 Choose **nce** or **nge** to complete each word. Write each word again.

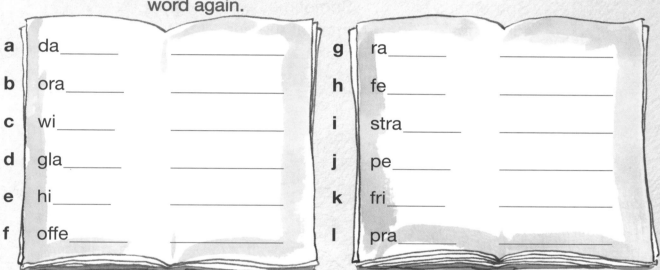

a da_____ _____

b ora_____ _____

c wi_____ _____

d gla_____ _____

e hi_____ _____

f offe_____ _____

g ra_____ _____

h fe_____ _____

i stra_____ _____

j pe_____ _____

k fri_____ _____

l pra_____ _____

Challenge 6 Match the pairs of short words to make some longer compound words.

sea		step
foot		noon
round		side	→ **c** _____seaside_____
run		ground
after		way
play		about

a _____

b _____

c _____seaside_____

d _____

e _____

f _____

You are progressing well!
Have an award sticker for your certificate.

Slithery Serpents

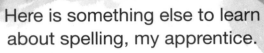

Here is something else to learn about spelling, my apprentice.

serpent   river

Sometimes er   Sometimes er
comes inside a   comes at the end
word.   of a word.

Task 1 Just do the best you can on this task, my apprentice. Make some **er** words.

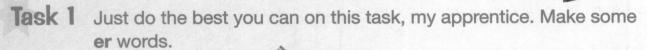

a k_er_b **b** j____k **c** v____se **d** s____ve **e** cam____a

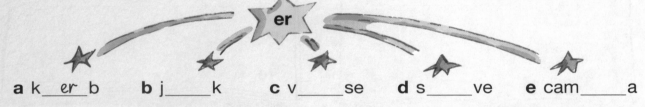

f s____pent **g** p____fume **h** obs____ve **i** int____est **j** diff____ent

Task 2 Now test your powers of observation! Write the words you made in Task 1 above in the right spaces.

a _k_ _e_ _r_ b   **e** _ _ s e r _ _   **h** p e r _ _ _ _

b _ _ _ s e   **f** _ _ r v _   **i** _ _ t e r _ _ _

c _ _ _ _ e r a   **g** j _ _ _   **j** _ _ _ _ _ _ n t

d _ _ f f _ _ _ _ _ _

Task 3 Do these **er** sums to make the names of jobs some people do.

a football + er = _____

d paint + er = _____

b clean + er = _____

e build + er = _____

c teach + er = _____

f garden + er = _____

Task 4 Make these verbs into nouns ending in **er**. Don't worry if it seems hard at first.

a skate _____skater_____

b bake _____

c dive _____

d tile _____

e dine _____

f hike _____

> When a verb ends with a **magic e**, you take off the **e**, then add **er** to make it into a noun.
> e.g. drive + **er** = driver

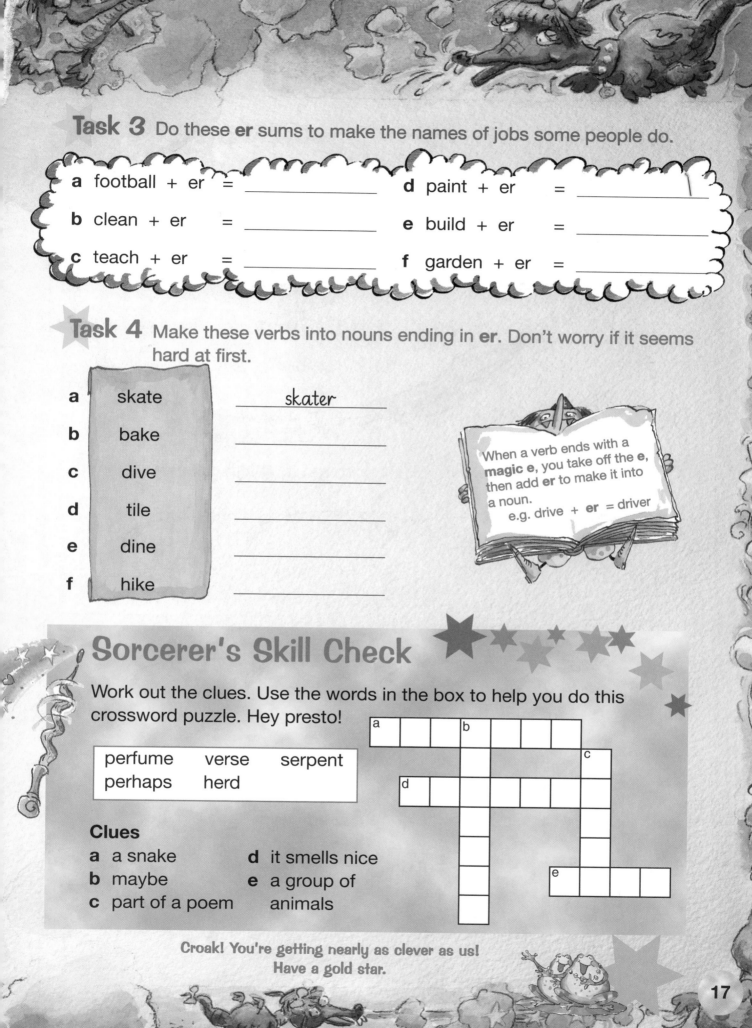

Sorcerer's Skill Check

Work out the clues. Use the words in the box to help you do this crossword puzzle. Hey presto!

| perfume | verse | serpent |
| perhaps | herd | |

Clues

a a snake   **d** it smells nice

b maybe   **e** a group of

c part of a poem   animals

Croak! You're getting nearly as clever as us!
Have a gold star.

Whirring and Stirring

Here's an interesting fact! In many words, ir sounds like er.

a thirsty bird

Task 1 Make some **ir** words. You'll soon get the hang of this!

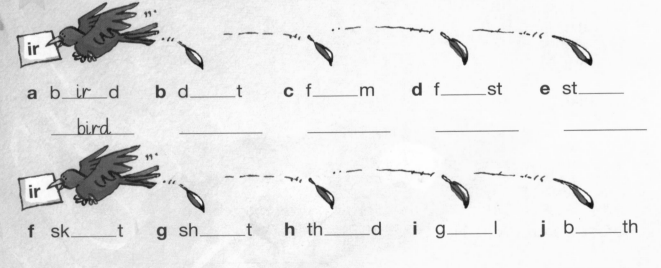

a b_ir_d   **b** d___t   **c** f___m   **d** f___st   **e** st___

___bird___   _____   _____   _____   _____

f sk___t   **g** sh___t   **h** th___d   **i** g___l   **j** b___th

_____   _____   _____   _____   _____

Task 2 Now try this. Write the correct word under each picture.

a   **b**   **c**   **d**

_____   _____   _____   _____

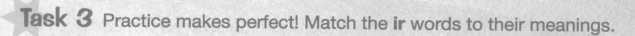

Task 3 Practice makes perfect! Match the **ir** words to their meanings.

| birthday | chirp | squirt | thirsty | thirteen | twirl | girder | birch |

a A type of tree   _____

b The day you were born   _____

c The number after twelve   _____

d To give something a spin   _____

e The noise birds make   _____

f This is how you feel when
you need a drink   _____

g A metal support used in building _____

h You do this with a water pistol _____

Task 4 Match up the pairs of rhyming words. It's easy when you know how!

shirt   mirth   stir   bird   whirl   thirty

fir   third   dirty   birth   squirt   girl

Sorcerer's Skill Check

Underline the hidden **ir** words. Super!

a qwyrtbirdcxz   **d** asdfirstfghj   **g** srvbirthbtrs

b asdfdirtghjk   **e** squirtyuioph   **h** hgfjuychirpd

c zfirmxcvbnml   **f** qwnrtyuthird   **i** zxthirstycvb

Oh dear! Have you finished already? You took me by surprise!
Have a gold star.

Perplexing Prefixes

A **prefix** is a **group of letters** we can add to the **beginning** of a word. Prefixes often change the **meanings** of words. When we add **un** or **dis** to a word it gives the word the **opposite** meaning.

tidy

<u>un</u>tidy

obedient

<u>dis</u>obedient

⭐ **Task 1** Now have a go at this exercise. Add the prefixes to make some new words.

a do _____undo_____   **e** place _____

b [un] cover _____   **f** [dis] able _____

c load _____   **g** agree _____

d wrap _____   **h** own _____

⭐ **Task 2** Take the prefix off each word. Write the word you are left with. Allakazan!

a unlock _____lock_____   **e** unhappy _____

b unpack _____   **f** unplug _____

c unlike _____   **g** disobey _____

d untidy _____   **h** disappear _____

Task 3 Do the best you can with this, my apprentice. Write the opposite of the underlined words in the gaps. Remember to use words with **un** and **dis** prefixes.

a The wizard made the rabbit <u>appear</u> and then _____ again.

b My bedroom is <u>tidy</u> but yours is _____.

c I am <u>happy</u> but you look very _____.

d My dog is very <u>obedient</u> but Sam's dog is _____.

e I <u>like</u> chips but I _____ sprouts.

f What Mark said was <u>true</u> but what Ben said was _____.

g This armchair is <u>comfortable</u> but that armchair is _____.

Task 4 Put a tick ✔ if the word has the correct prefix. Put a cross ✗ if it is wrong. Hey presto!

a disdo ☆   **d** unwell ☆   **g** disappear ☆   **j** unkind ☆

b untrust ☆   **e** disagree ☆   **h** unwrap ☆   **k** unhonest ☆

c unfair ☆   **f** unload ☆   **i** disbolt ☆   **l** unusual ☆

Sorcerer's Skill Check

Abracadabra! Do some magic and write the opposite of each word by adding the prefix **un** or **dis**.

a _____do   **b** _____obey   **c** _____load   **d** _____please

e _____pack   **f** _____usual   **g** _____trust   **h** _____well

Super stuff! You have earned a gold star for persistence.

Fascinating ing

Oh dear! When you add **ing** to the end of some words it gets a little confusing! I think I understand it, so I will try and explain!

dazzle – dazzling

When we add **ing** to a verb ending in a consonant + e we drop the e before adding the ending.

Task 1   Please help me to complete these verbs.

a m__ake__   **b** w_____   **c** t_____   **d** b_____   **e** r_____

f g__ive__   **g** l_____   **h** d_____   **i** dr_____   **j** forg_____

k h__ope__   **l** c_____   **m** m_____   **n** sl_____   **o** gr_____

Task 2   I'm a little mixed up! Can you help me? Drop the **e** and add **ing** to all the verbs you made in Task 1 above.

ake words   **a** __making__   **b** _____   **c** _____   **d** _____   **e** _____

ive words   **f** __giving__   **g** _____   **h** _____   **i** _____   **j** _____

ope words   **k** __hoping__   **l** _____   **m** _____   **n** _____   **o** _____

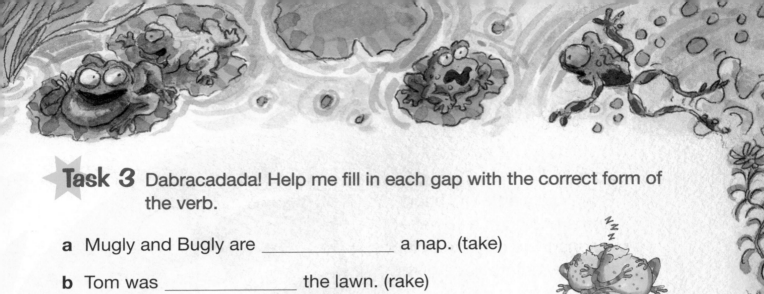

Task 3 Dabracadada! Help me fill in each gap with the correct form of the verb.

a Mugly and Bugly are _____ a nap. (take)

b Tom was _____ the lawn. (rake)

c I am _____ a cake. (bake)

d Do you like _____ presents? (give)

e I am _____ in London. (live)

f Mr Shah was _____ his car. (drive)

g I was _____ to see you soon. (hope)

h I am _____ because I was told off. (mope)

i The ground was _____ . (slope)

j Is the wizard _____ his wand? (wave)

Sorcerer's Skill Check

Oh dear! I thought we had finished, but there is still one activity for you to help me with! Complete the spell book for me.

a smoke _____smoking_____   **f** _____fade_____ fading

b ride _____   **g** _____ noting

c skate _____   **h** _____ smiling

d use _____   **i** _____ taming

e wave _____   **j** _____ telephoning

Slurp! Help yourself to a gold star, if you've got time!
We're off for a nap!

Doubling Up

Brain cell alert! With short words ending in a vowel + a consonant we often double the last letter before adding ing.

hop – hopping

We like to hop.
We like hopping.

Task 1 Croak! Make each of these into a verb ending in **ing**.

a	tap	_tapping_	**e**	dot	_____	**i**	sob	_____
b	jam	_____	**f**	pop	_____	**j**	hit	_____
c	shop	_____	**g**	fan	_____	**k**	pad	_____
d	zip	_____	**h**	win	_____	**l**	trap	_____

Task 2 This looks like a job for Pointy! Take off the **ing** and leave the short form of each verb.

a	hopping	_hop_	**e**	dipping	_____	**i**	letting	_____
b	pinning	_____	**f**	fitting	_____	**j**	nodding	_____
c	robbing	_____	**g**	rotting	_____	**k**	putting	_____
d	batting	_____	**h**	humming	_____	**l**	betting	_____

Task 3 Write each sentence under the correct picture, while we have a snooze!

| I like batting. | I like robbing. | I like hopping. | I like winning. |
| I like shopping. | I like chatting. | I like drumming. | I like clapping. |

a _____

d _____

g _____

b _____

e _____

h _____

c _____

f _____

Sorcerer's Skill Check

Grub's up! Choose the correct verb to complete each sentence.

a Pointy is _____ a nail into the wall. (taping/tapping)

b The girl is _____ from stone to stone. (hoping/hopping)

c The teacher is _____ up a picture. (pining/pinning)

d The child is _____ the race. (wining/winning)

e The burglar was _____ the house. (robing/robbing)

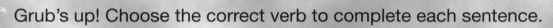

Well tried, my apprentice. Your spelling is coming on nicely!
Award yourself a gold star.

Puzzling Plurals

Try to remember that singular means one and plural means more than one.
Here are two rules to help you learn how to spell plurals correctly.

One dish. Lots of dishes!

One fly. Lots of flies!

RULE 1
When a word ends in s, x, ch or sh, we add es in the plural.

RULE 2
When a word ends in a consonant + y, we change the y to i and add es.

Task 1 Complete this parchment, my apprentice. Use Rule 1 to help you.

singular	plural	singular	plural
a one fox	lots of _foxes_	**e** one dress	lots of _____
b one watch	lots of _____	**f** one brush	lots of _____
c one wish	lots of _____	**g** one bench	lots of _____
d one branch	lots of _____	**h** one box	lots of _____

Task 2 Now have a go at this parchment. Use Rule 1 again to help you.

singular	plural	singular	plural
a one _____	lots of bushes	**e** one _____	lots of arches
b one _____	lots of bosses	**f** one _____	lots of asses
c one _____	lots of boxes	**g** one _____	lots of torches
d one _____	lots of stitches	**h** one _____	lots of lashes

Task 3

Hey presto! Write the plural form of the word under each picture. Use Rule 2 to help you. Allakazan!

a baby	**b** lady	**c** lorry	**d** cherry

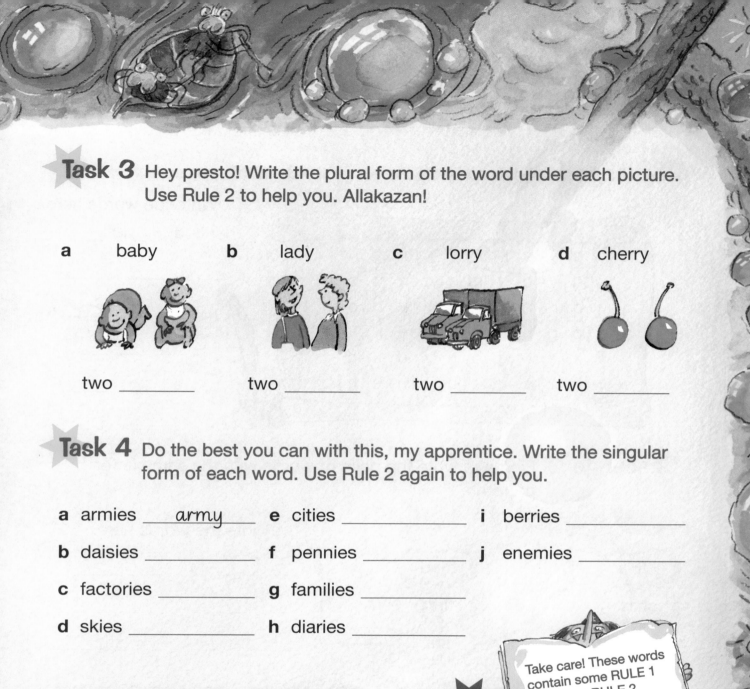

two _____   two _____   two _____   two _____

Task 4

Do the best you can with this, my apprentice. Write the singular form of each word. Use Rule 2 again to help you.

a armies ___army___   **e** cities _____   **i** berries _____

b daisies _____   **f** pennies _____   **j** enemies _____

c factories _____   **g** families _____

d skies _____   **h** diaries _____

Take care! These words contain some RULE 1 and some RULE 2 words mixed up.

Sorcerer's Skill Check

Allakazan! Write the plural form of each word.

a one fairy but two _____   **e** one body but two _____

b one kiss but two _____   **f** one fox but two _____

c one bunch but two _____   **g** one arch but two _____

d one match but two _____   **h** one marsh but two _____

You have been awarded another gold star! You are getting to be as clever as Pointy!

Apprentice Wizard Challenge 2

Challenge 1   Find and circle the six **er** words in this puzzle.

Write the words here.

a _____ jerk _____

b _____

c _____

d _____

e _____

f _____

```
a b c j e r k d n f g h j k
z x d v b n m s e r v e l x
q w o r k e r b t y u o p b
a s d g h f a r m e r k v c
b a k e r c b n z d k h g h
w v h a s t e a c h e r p m
```

Challenge 2   Find and write the pairs of words with the same letter patterns.

Write the words here.

fir   third   a _____   _____

shirt   first   b _____   _____

bird   stir   c _____ fir _____   _____ stir _____

thirst   twirl   d _____   _____

girl   skirt   e _____   _____

Challenge 3   Add **un** or **dis** to these words to make them mean the opposite.

a _____tidy   d _____well   g _____connect   j _____agree

b _____obey   e _____please   h _____common   k _____colour

c _____do   f _____trust   i _____true   l _____comfortable

28

Challenge 4 Take off the **ing**. Write correctly the verb you are left with.

a smoking – ing = _smoke_ **f** hating – ing = _____

b shaking – ing = _____ **g** liking – ing = _____

c framing – ing = _____ **h** piling – ing = _____

d blaming – ing = _____ **i** diving – ing = _____

e gaping – ing = _____ **j** sloping – ing = _____

Challenge 5 Complete each sentence with the **ing** form of the verb in brackets.

a I like _____ . (hop) **f** I like _____ . (chat)

b I like _____ . (clap) **g** I like _____ . (drum)

c I like _____ . (hum) **h** I don't like _____ . (sob)

d I like _____ . (win) **i** I don't like _____ . (bet)

e I like _____ . (bat) **j** I don't like _____ . (slip)

Challenge 6 Complete this parchment:

singular	plural	singular	plural
a glass	_____	**f** _____	foxes
b arch	_____	**g** _____	brushes
c baby	_____	**h** _____	flies
d boss	_____	**i** _____	taxes
e torch	_____	**j** _____	fairies

**You have done exceptionally well, my apprentice!
Another gold star for you is in order!**

Answers

Pages 2–3

Task 1 **a** owl   **e** hen
b otter   **f** ant
c bat   **g** duck
d rat   **h** ape

Task 2 **a** cat (or bat)   **d** seal
b dog   **e** camel
c goat   **f** badger

Task 3 Answers may include:
a pot, at, to   **d** rout, out
b car, rot   **e** turn, nip
c on   **f** if, flow, flower, low, lower

Task 4 Answers may include:
a for, or, fort, able, table, tab, comfort
b band, and, age, ban, an
c star, tar, are
d at, ten, on, tent
e be, cause, us, use
f beat, eat, eaten, ten, at, ate

Sorcerer's Skill Check
a call   **b** pink
c band   **d** cluck

Pages 4–5

Task 1 **a** beast, feast   **d** tea, sea
b heap, leap   **e** beat, heat
c weak, leak

Task 2 **a** feather, weather
d wealthy, healthy
c death, breath
b head, instead
e ready, steady

Task 3 **a** neat   **f** leather
b heavy   **g** beast
c meadow   **h** cream
d steam   **i** deaf
e jealous   **j** speak

Task 4 **short ea:** heavy, meadow, jealous, leather, deaf
long ea: neat, steam, beast, cream, speak

Sorcerer's Skill Check
a brĕad   **g** swĕat
b bēat   **h** trĕad
c hēap   **i** wēak
d thread   **j** tēach
e fēast   **k** wĕather
f ēagle   **l** alrĕady

Pages 6–7

Task 1 **a** cow   **b** town
c owl   **d** gown

Task 2 **a** low   **b** slow
c bowl   **d** snow

Task 3 **ow sounds like crow:** low, mow, snow, slow, shown, blow
ow sounds like owl: now, how, brown, cow, growl, crown

Sorcerer's Skill Check
a cow   **d** snow
b owl   **e** tower
c bowl   **f** mower

Pages 8–9

Task 1 **a** cook   **e** hood
b book   **f** wood
c hook   **g** good
d rook   **h** stood

Task 2 **a** a cookery book
b Red Riding Hood in the wood

Task 3 took, look, woods, hoods, stood, rooks, brook, foot, shook

Task 4 **a** took, look, rooks, brook, shook
b woods, hoods, stood
c foot

Sorcerer's Skill Check
a look   **g** book, boot
b foot, food   **h** took, toot
c brook, brood   **i** cook
d good   **j** wood
e soot   **k** crook
f blood   **l** rook, root

Pages 10–11

Task 1 **a** nice, slice, twice, rice
b face, place, space, race
c rage, cage, page, wage

Task 2 **a** nice slice
b cage
c space
d twice, face

Task 3 **a** hinge
b dance
c fence
d orange

Task 4 **nce words (orange stars):** a, c, d, g, i
nge words (blue stars): b, e, f, h, j

Sorcerer's Skill Check
a dice   **i** twice
b mice   **j** office
c cage   **k** stage
d page   **l** courage
e slice   **m** police
f price   **n** message
g sage   **o** average
h wage

Pages 12–13

Task 1 **a** snowman   **f** horseshoe
b butterfly   **g** ladybird
c football   **h** keyhole
d windmill   **i** sheepdog
e pancake   **j** sunshine

Task 2 **a** horseshoe   **b** butterfly
c windmill   **d** pancake

Task 3 **a** seesaw   **e** motorway
b waterfall   **f** airport
c farmyard   **g** friendship
d bathroom   **h** hairdresser

Sorcerer's Skill Check
a birth + day
b farm + yard
c wall + paper
d butter + cup
e out + side
f cloak + room
g dish + cloth
h break + fast
i in + doors
j my + self

Pages 14–15

Challenge 1
a every   **g** father
b suddenly   **h** know
c want   **i** many
d down   **j** friend
e monkey   **k** because
f shout   **l** yellow

Challenge 2
a heavy   **e** deaf
b neat   **f** peach
c meadow   **g** cream
d leather   **h** speak

Challenge 3
a grow   **b** town
c crowd   **d** throw

Challenge 4
a cook   **f** nook
b took   **g** shook
c hook   **h** crook
d rook   **i** brook
e book

Challenge 5
a dance   **g** range
b orange   **h** fence
c wince   **i** strange
d glance   **j** pence
e hinge   **k** fringe
f offence   **l** prance

Challenge 6
a footstep   **d** playground
b afternoon   **e** runway
c seaside   **f** roundabout

Pages 16–17

Task 1 **a** kerb   **f** serpent
b jerk   **g** perfume
c verse   **h** observe
d serve   **i** interest
e camera   **j** different

Task 2 **a** kerb   **f** serve
b verse   **g** jerk
c camera   **h** perfume
d different   **i** interest
e observe   **j** serpent

Task 3 **a** footballer   **d** painter
b cleaner   **e** builder
c teacher   **f** gardener

Task 4 **a** skater   **d** tiler
b baker   **e** diner
c diver   **f** hiker

a serpent **d** perfume
b perhaps **e** herd
c verse

★ Pages 18–19

Task 1
a bird **f** skirt
b dirt **g** shirt
c firm **h** third
d first **i** girl
e stir **j** birth

Task 2
a shirt **b** skirt
c girl **d** bird

Task 3
a birch **e** chirp
b birthday **f** thirsty
c thirteen **g** girder
d twirl **h** squirt

Task 4 shirt-squirt; mirth-birth; stir-fir;
bird-third; whirl-girl; thirty-dirty

Sorcerer's Skill Check

a bird **f** third
b dirt **g** birth
c firm **h** chirp
d first **i** thirsty
e squirt

★ Pages 20–21

Task 1
a undo **e** displace
b uncover **f** disable
c unload **g** disagree
d unwrap **h** disown

Task 2
a lock **e** happy
b pack **f** plug
c like **g** obey
d tidy **h** appear

Task 3
a disappear **e** dislike
b untidy **f** untrue
c unhappy **g** uncomfortable
d disobedient

Task 4 correct words: c, d, e, f, g, h, j, l

Sorcerer's Skill Check

a undo **e** unpack
b disobey **f** unusual
c unload **g** distrust
d displease **h** unwell

★ Pages 22–23

Task 1
a make **i** drive
b wake **j** forgive
c take **k** hope
d bake **l** cope
e rake **m** mope
f give **n** slope
g live **o** grope
h dive

Task 2
a making **i** driving
b waking **j** forgiving
c taking **k** hoping
d baking **l** coping
e raking **m** moping
f giving **n** sloping
g living **o** groping
h diving

Task 3
a taking **f** driving
b raking **g** hoping
c baking **h** moping
d giving **i** sloping
e living **j** waving

Sorcerer's Skill Check

a smoking **f** fade
b riding **g** note
c skating **h** smile
d using **i** tame
e waving **j** telephone

★ Pages 24–25

Task 1
a tapping **g** fanning
b jamming **h** winning
c shopping **i** sobbing
d zipping **j** hitting
e dotting **k** padding
f popping **l** trapping

Task 2
a hop **g** rot
b pin **h** hum
c rob **i** let
d bat **j** nod
e dip **k** put
f fit **l** bet

Task 3
a I like chatting.
b I like hopping.
c I like winning.
d I like batting.
e I like clapping.
f I like shopping.
g I like drumming.
h I like robbing.

Sorcerer's Skill Check

a tapping **d** winning
b hopping **e** robbing
c pinning

★ Pages 26–27

Task 1
a foxes **e** dresses
b watches **f** brushes
c wishes **g** benches
d branches **h** boxes

Task 2
a bush **e** arch
b boss **f** ass
c box **g** torch
d stitch **h** lash

Task 3
a babies **b** ladies
c lorries **d** cherries

Task 4
a army **f** penny
b daisy **g** family
c factory **h** diary
d sky **i** berry
e city **j** enemy

Sorcerer's Skill Check

a fairies **e** bodies
b kisses **f** foxes
c bunches **g** arches
d matches **h** marshes

★ Pages 28–29

Challenge 1
a jerk **d** farmer
b serve **e** baker
c worker **f** teacher

Challenge 2
a bird-third **d** girl-twirl
b thirst-first **e** shirt-skirt
c fir-stir

Challenge 3
a untidy **g** disconnect
b disobey **h** uncommon
c undo **i** untrue
d unwell **j** disagree
e displease **k** discolour
f distrust **l** uncomfortable

Challenge 4
a smoke **f** hate
b shake **g** like
c frame **h** pile
d blame **i** dive
e gape **j** slope

Challenge 5
a hopping **f** chatting
b clapping **g** drumming
c humming **h** sobbing
d winning **i** betting
e batting **j** slipping

Challenge 6
a glasses **f** fox
b arches **g** brush
c babies **h** fly
d bosses **i** tax
e torches **j** fairy

Wizard's Certificate of Excellence

⭐ **Wiggly Words**

⭐ **Slithery Serpents**

⭐ **Fearless Feats**

⭐ **Whirring and Stirring**

⭐ **Scowling Shadows**

⭐ **Perplexing Prefixes**

⭐ **Hooks and Books**

⭐ **Fascinating ing**

⭐ **Strange Spaces**

⭐ **Doubling Up**

⭐ **Conjuring Compounds**

⭐ **Puzzling Plurals**

⭐ **Apprentice Wizard Challenge 1**

⭐ **Apprentice Wizard Challenge 2**

This is to state that Wizard Whimstaff awards

Apprentice —————————————————

the title of English Wizard. Congratulations!

Wizard Whimstaff

Published 2002
10 9 8 7 6

Letts Educational, The Chiswick Centre,
414 Chiswick High Road, London W4 5TF
Tel 020 8996 3333   Fax 020 8742 8390
Email mail@lettsed.co.uk
www.letts-education.com

Text, design and illustrations © Letts Educational Ltd 2002

Author: Louis Fidge
Book Concept and Development:
Helen Jacobs, Publishing Director
Sophie London, Project Editor
Design and Editorial: 2idesign, Cambridge
Cover Design: Linda Males
Illustrations: Mike Phillips and Neil Chapman (Beehive illustration)
Cover Illustration: Neil Chapman

Letts Educational Limited is a division of Granada Learning Limited.
Part of Granada plc.

British Library Cataloguing in Publication Data

A CIP record for this book is available from the British Library.

ISBN 1 84315 110 3

Printed in Italy

Colour reproduction by PDQ Digital Media Solutions Ltd, Bungay, Suffolk.